This book belongs to:

Danilynn Mariah Felle

An Imprint of Sterling Publishing
387 Park Avenue South
New York, NY 10016

Text © 2013 by QEB Publishing, Inc.
Illustrations © 2013 by QEB Publishing, Inc.

This 2013 edition published by Sandy Creek.

Consultant: Barbara Taylor
Editor: Lauren Taylor
Designer: Elaine Wilkinson

ISBN 978-1-4351-4401-9

Library of Congress Cataloging-in-Publication Data

Loughrey, Anita.
 Autumn with squirrel / by Anita Loughrey ; illustrated by Daniel Howarth.
    p. cm. -- (Animal seasons)
 ISBN 978-1-60992-227-6 (hardcover, library bound)
 1. Autumn--Juvenile literature. 2. Squirrels--Juvenile literature. I. Howarth, Daniel. II. Title.
 QB637.7.L68 2012
 508.2--dc23
                                    2011050870

Manufactured in Guangdong, China
Lot #:
4 6 8 10 9 7 5 3
05/14

Squirrel's Fall Search

Anita Loughrey
and Daniel Howarth

Sandy Creek
NEW YORK

Squirrel and his little brother were busy
collecting pine cones, berries, and nuts.

Fall had arrived and food was everywhere.

Juicy blackberries speckled
the thorny bushes.

Corn was being harvested in the cornfield.

Squirrel's little brother picked up
one of Squirrel's nuts.
"I bet you can't catch me!" he laughed,
and then he ran away.

They chased each other around in circles.
Colorful leaves swirled all around
and made Squirrel dizzy.

Squirrel chased his little
brother into the woods.

But soon he realized he could
not see his little brother
or his food anywhere.

Squirrel hoped his little brother wasn't taking any more of his nuts!

Mouse scampered out of the leaves
carrying a seed.

Squirrel started to feel hungry.

Squirrel had enjoyed chasing his
brother so much that he had forgotten
where he had put his food.

"Have you seen my food?" Squirrel asked Mouse.
"Have you looked in the meadow?" asked Mouse.

Squirrel searched the long
grass in the meadow.
He tutted and scratched his head.

"I'm sure my food was around here somewhere," he said.

Rabbit poked his head
out of his hole to see
what was going on.

"Have you seen my food anywhere?"
asked Squirrel.

"Have you looked by the pond?"
suggested Rabbit.

Squirrel searched through the reeds by the pond.
Leaves were floating on the surface of the water.
Squirrel sniffed the air and tutted.

"I'm sure I buried my food around here somewhere," he said.

Owl was watching Squirrel from above. "Isn't that your little brother over there by the old apple tree?" she asked.

"It looks like he's got some tasty food to eat!"
said Owl.

Squirrel ran as fast as he could to the apple tree.

Squirrel's little brother was so surprised that he dropped the nut he was holding.

"I'm sorry," he said. "I was just so hungry."

"Did you know," said Squirrel,
"that food tastes even better if you share it?"

They smiled at each other
and ate their tasty food together.

Fall Activities

Fun and simple ideas
for you to explore.

What food is harvested in fall?
Lots of different types of food are available
for picking and harvesting during fall.
What types of food are harvested where
you live? Name the foods that
appear in the story.

Go for a fall walk. The fall is a great time for
a walk. The weather isn't too hot or too cold,
and it's fun to play in the leaves.
It's also a good time to collect pine cones
and leaves for home craft projects. On
your walk, collect as many different
colored leaves as you can.

Make a leaf collage. Use the leaves you collected from your fall walk. For best results, make sure the leaves are completely dry before using them. You can glue them onto cardstock in any pattern you like. You could even try using wax crayons to make leaf rubbings.

Act out the story. Use paper, pens, pencils, and paints to make masks of Squirrel and his friends. Can you remember anything the characters said? You could either act out the story as it is in the book, or you might prefer to add a twist.

What Did We Learn About Fall?

The woods and fields are full of food. Fall is a season when there is plenty of food, such as berries and nuts. Animals eat as much as they can to build up stores of body fat. They use this fat to help them stay warm in the winter.

Squirrel and his little brother are collecting food. Some animals store food in the fall. They bury the food in the soil, or hide it inside holes. They go back to these hiding places to eat the food during the winter.

Corn is being harvested in the cornfield. Fall is a busy time of year for farmers. They harvest the crops growing in the fields or on fruit trees, and start planting new crops for the following year.

Squirrel chases his little brother in the colorful, falling leaves. As the fall days get colder, the leaves on some trees turn different shades of red, brown, and yellow. This is because the green color in the leaves breaks down so we can see the other colors hidden underneath. Fall winds blow the dry leaves off the trees.

Geese are flying over the woods. In the fall, some birds go on a long migration journey to spend the winter in a warmer place, such as Africa. They will return to their home country when the weather warms up in the spring.